THE CHILDREN'S BOOK OF BOOKS

THE CHILDREN'S BOOK OF BOOKS

In celebration of

WORLD BOOK DAY

1998

Published in association with
PENGUIN BOOKS LTD
and
RANDOM HOUSE UK LTD

The Children's Book of Books *has been compiled and produced by Penguin Books Ltd and Random House UK Ltd*

PENGUIN BOOKS LTD/RANDOM HOUSE UK LTD

Penguin Books Ltd, Registered Offices: Harmondsworth, Middlesex, England
Random House UK Ltd, Registered Offices: 20 Vauxhall Bridge Road, London, England

First published 1998

This compilation copyright © Penguin Books Ltd, 1998

The acknowledgements on pages 156–8 constitute an extension of this copyright page

Printed free of charge for World Book Day in Great Britain by:
Caledonian International Book Manufacturing Ltd
Clays Ltd, St Ives plc
Cox & Wyman Ltd
Mackays of Chatham plc

Sponsors of World Book Day

World Book Day 1998 is an initiative sponsored by booksellers and publishers, the Department for Education and Employment, the Qualifications and Curriculum Authority and the Basic Skills Agency.

The following organizations have also contributed:
The Booksellers' Association of Great Britain and Ireland; the Publishers' Association; the Arts Council of England; the BBC; Book Tokens Ltd; the Royal Literary Fund.

Publishers
Major contributors: BBC Books; HarperCollins Publishers; Hodder Headline plc; Little, Brown and Company; Macmillan Publishers Ltd; Oxford University Press; Penguin Books Ltd; Random House UK Ltd; Scholastic Ltd; Transworld Publishers Ltd.

Other contributors: Andersen Press Ltd; A & C Black (Publishers) Ltd; Bloomsbury Publishing plc; British Museum Press; Constable & Co Ltd; David Campbell Publishing; Dorling Kindersley Ltd; Element Books; Evans Brothers Ltd; Faber & Faber Ltd; Fourth Estate Ltd; C. Hurst & Co (Publishers) Ltd; Larousse plc; John Murray (Publishers) Ltd; Simon and Schuster; Sutton Publishing Ltd; Two-Can Publishing; Usborne Publishing; Virgin Publishing Ltd; Walker Books Ltd.

Booksellers
Most booksellers in the UK and Ireland are supporting World Book Day, but particularly the following: Bertrams the Book Wholesaler; Blackwell Retail Ltd; Books Etc Ltd; Dillons The Bookstore; Gardners Books Ltd; Hammicks Bookshops Ltd; W. Heffer & Sons Ltd; John Menzies (UK) Ltd; John Smith & Son Ltd; Lomond Books; Ottakar's plc; Sussex Stationers plc; THE Books; Waterstone's Booksellers Ltd; W. H. Smith Ltd.

Book Clubs
The Book People Ltd, Book Club Associates.

Printers and Manufacturers
Abitibi Consolidated; BKH Paper Convertors Ltd; Borregaard Hellefos A S, Norway; Caledonian International Book Manufacturing Ltd; Clark Stephen Packaging Services Ltd; Clays Ltd, St Ives plc; Concise Cover Printers Ltd; Cox & Wyman Ltd; Denmaur Papers plc; Enso Publication Papers' Anjala Mill; Iggesbund Board Sales Ltd; Mackays of Chatham plc; Metsa-Serla Paperboard Ltd; Norske Skog (A/S Union) Ltd; Paper Management Services Ltd; Spectrum Press (Northampton) Ltd; UPM-Kymmene Ltd; Yale Press Ltd.

Distributors
Securicor Omega Express; The Book Service.

Contents

Foreword

Books give pleasure and enjoyment to millions of people. They are also a vital source of knowledge and learning whatever the age of the reader. World Book Day aims to remind everyone that it's good to read.

This book has been specially prepared for World Book Day, 23 April 1998. All the celebrities who have sent in their suggestions have found reading an enjoyable and memorable experience and now want to share their favourite books with you. We hope you enjoy the extracts from their best reads and compare their choices with your own. If there are selections from books you haven't read, it might be a good idea to find a copy of the book and see if you agree with the person who chose it.

On World Book Day 1998 there is much more happening. Every child and young person in school that day will receive a £1 book voucher so that they can buy a book. The voucher can be exchanged for *The Children's Book of Books* or can be used towards the purchase of any other book.

This year, there are many other events and celebrations going on for World Book Day, in libraries, schools and theatres and on television and radio.

The publishers, booksellers and distributors who have organized all this, hope you will enjoy the day and remember how exciting and important it is to carry on reading.

Time for Play
Age 0-5

from Five Minutes' Peace
by Jill Murphy

*All Mrs Large the elephant wants to do is relax
in her bath and have five minutes' peace.
But Lester, Laura and 'the little one' have
got other plans . . .*

In came Laura. 'Can I read you a page from my reading book?' she asked.

'No, Laura,' said Mrs Large. 'Go on, *all* of you, off downstairs.'

'You let Lester play his tune,' said Laura. 'I heard. You like him better than me. It's not fair.'

'Oh, don't be silly, Laura,' said Mrs Large. 'Go *on* then. Just *one* page.'

So Laura read. She read four and a half pages of 'Little Red Riding Hood'.

In came the little one with a trunkful of toys. 'For *you!*' he beamed, flinging them all into the bath water.

'Thank you, dear,' said Mrs Large weakly.

'Can I see the cartoons in the paper?' asked Laura.

'Can I have the cake?' asked Lester.

'Can I get in with you?' asked the little one.

Mrs Large groaned.

In the end they *all* got in. The little one was in such a hurry that he forgot to take off his pyjamas.

Mrs Large got out. She dried herself, put on her dressing-gown and headed for the door.

'Where are you going *now*, Mum?' asked Laura.

'To the kitchen,' said Mrs Large.

'Why?' asked Lester.

'Because I want five minutes' peace from *you* lot,' said Mrs Large. 'That's why.'

---

*OK – they're elephants. But they're a real family. They slop around, things go wrong, things are out of place – but the family sees it through. Great illustrations, too – **Ainsley Harriott***

from Owl at Home
by Arnold Lobel
(I Can Read series)

*Owl wants to make a pot of tea with a
difference — tear-water tea. So he makes himself
think of some very sad things . . .*

'Chairs with broken legs,' said Owl. His eyes
began to water.

◊

'Songs that cannot be sung,' said Owl, 'because
the words have been forgotten.'

◊

Owl began to cry. A large tear rolled down
and dropped into the kettle.

◊

'Spoons that have fallen behind the stove and
are never seen again,' said Owl.

◊

More tears dropped down into the kettle.

◊

'Books that cannot be read,' said Owl,
'because some of the pages have been torn out.'

◊

'Clocks that have stopped,' said Owl, 'with no one near to wind them up.'

◊

Owl was crying. Many large tears dropped into the kettle.

◊

'Mornings nobody saw because everybody was sleeping,' sobbed Owl.

◊

'Mashed potatoes left on a plate,' he cried, 'because no one wanted to eat them. And pencils that are too short to use.'

◊

Owl thought about many other sad things. He cried and cried. Soon the kettle was all filled up with tears.

First, I had the great pleasure of reading it, over and over, to my daughter. Then, she had the great pleasure – and triumph *– of reading it, faster and faster, back to me –* **Anne Fine**

Incy Wincy Spider
Traditional nursery rhyme

Incy Wincy Spider climbed up the water spout,
(Use the fingers of both hands to represent a spider climbing up.)
Down came the rain drops and washed poor Incy out;
(Raise the hands and lower them slowly, wriggling fingers to indicate rain.)
Out came the sunshine and dried up all the rain,
(Raise hands above the head together and bring them out and down.)
And Incy Wincy Spider climbed up that spout again.
(As first line.)

*We enjoy traditional nursery rhymes because Elliot, who is three, can join in, especially 'Incy Wincy Spider', which is his favourite. It reminds me of when I was young, too – **Sharron Davies***

Chosen by
Emma Forbes, TV presenter

The Very Hungry Caterpillar
by Eric Carle

This is the story of a very small and very hungry caterpillar. He eats one apple on Monday, two pears on Tuesday, three plums on Wednesday, four strawberries on Thursday, five oranges on Friday, and on Saturday he has an enormous feast. The caterpillar grows from a small egg to a beautiful butterfly and at the same time manages to nibble his way through the pages of the book!

Because my daughter's only ten months old, it's a great introduction to reading – as it's bright, colourful, easy to read and a sweet story
– Emma Forbes

from Dogger
by Shirley Hughes

When Dave's favourite toy, Dogger, disappears, his family search everywhere. But Dogger can't be found – that is, until the day of the garden fête.

One lady had a Toy Stall, full of knitted ducks and cars and baby dolls in bonnets. And there, at the very back of the stall, behind a lot of other toys, was – DOGGER!

He was wearing a ticket saying '5p'.

There were a lot of people round the stall. Dave tried to explain to the lady that it was his Dogger, who had got lost and somehow been put on the stall by mistake, but she wasn't listening. He looked in his pocket. He had 3p but that wasn't enough. He ran to find Mum and Dad to ask them to buy Dogger back *at once*.

Dave went everywhere in the crowd but he couldn't see Mum and Dad. He thought he was going to cry. At last he found Bella by the cakes. When she heard about Dogger, she and Dave ran back to the Toy Stall as fast as they could.

Quack! Who's in
the Country?
(*Heads and Tails series*)

Twit! Twooo! Who's that?
A strange noise, the tip of a tail, the end of a nose . . . these are the kinds of clues found in this lift-the-flap book adventure. Animals of the countryside are then revealed beneath the flaps.

When it says 'Tap! Tap! Tap! Who's that?' my children, Carys and Etta, both like to tap on the flap very hard with their pointed fingers, before revealing the funny woodpecker underneath –
Trevor Neal

Top Books

The Baby Who Wouldn't Go to Bed by Helen Cooper won the Kate Greenaway Medal in 1996. This prize is awarded for outstanding illustration in a children's book.

The Baby wants to stay up all night, so he revs up his car and sets off on an adventure. Before long, he finds himself all alone in a sleepy land where his favourite toys come to life. But they're all too tired to play and he soon feels sleepy too. When Mother comes to tuck him up in bed it's time to say goodnight.

Guess How Much I Love You by Sam McBratney and Anita Jeram was the bestselling children's picture book in high street bookshops in 1997. (Source: Booktrack)

Guess How Much I Love You tells the story of Little Nutbrown Hare, who is trying to tell Big Nutbrown Hare how much he loves him. He shows how wide he can stretch his paws, how high he can reach and how far he can hop, but none of these is quite enough. As both

Little Nutbrown Hare and Big Nutbrown Hare discover, love is a very difficult thing to measure.

> *Drop Dead* by Babette Cole won the Kurt Maschler Award in 1996. This prize is given for the use of imagination in a children's book.

When asked why they are bald and wrinkly, Gran and Grandad set off on a wonderful recall of their entire lives, which have been more colourful than anyone can possibly imagine. Having reached old age, in spite of their hair-raising adventures, they expect one day to drop down dead like everyone else. But they are in for one final surprise.

from Green Eggs and Ham
by Dr Seuss

Sam-I-am has a plate of delicious food for someone to eat. But is there anyone who likes green eggs and ham?

Would you, could you, in the rain?
I would not, could not, in the rain.
Not in the dark. Not on a train.
Not in a car. Not in a tree.
I do not like them, Sam, you see.
Not in a house. Not in a box.
Not with a mouse. Not with a fox.
I will not eat them here or there.
I do not like them anywhere!
You do not like green eggs and ham?
I do not like them, Sam-I-am.

from Schnitzel von Krumm's Basketwork
by Lynley Dodd

*Schnitzel von Krumm, the little
dachshund dog, is outraged when his misguided
family decides to replace his worn-out,
smelly old basket.*

'YUK!' said his family,
  'Time to say no –
this beaten-up basket
must INSTANTLY go.
It's scruffy
and dirty,
it's hopelessly small
and we really can't have
such a smell
in the hall.'
So they lifted the basket
and took it away
and bought him another
the very same day.

He tried it for size;
there was room for his tum
but it didn't smell friendly
to Schnitzel von Krumm.
The basket was smart
and a much better fit –
was it cosy and comforting?
NO
not a bit.

> *Beautifully written and illustrated. A lovely, simple story which my children can join in reading with never-ending enthusiasm – **Sally Whittaker***

*Let's Go Swimming with
Mr Silly Pants*
by M. K. Brown
was the choice of **Alastair Campbell**,
Chief Press Secretary, 10 Downing Street

> *It is colourful, funny, bears retelling and all three of my children have enjoyed it in exactly the same way, at the same age – **Alastair Campbell***

Grunty the Pig
by S. G. Hulme-Beaman
(*Out of the Ark series*)

(This character was created in 1927.)

Grunty the Pig lives in the Ark with Mr and Mrs Noah and all the other animals. In one of the stories, naughty Polar the Bear and Grunty take a tin of treacle and a bowl of potatoes from the kitchen. Greedy Grunty gobbles up all the treacle and potatoes – and then nobody can understand why he isn't hungry at dinner time. A doctor is called for, but the truth eventually comes out and Grunty is sent to bed.

> *Grunty the Pig was greedy – pigs often are. He told lies and he got his friend into trouble . . . but he made me laugh. He still does!*
> *– Jean Adamson*

from Rupert
the Bear
by Alfred Bestall

The cycle glides high in the air.
Oh! What a thrill for Rupert Bear.

The cloud banks end and at great pace,
Poor Rupert shoots off into space.

Then Rupert sees with great delight,
Two wings appear to help his flight.

My 1945 Rupert Bear Annual *contains magic,
adventure, wonder, humour, surrealism, friendship
and a bicycle that climbs trees and flies – forty
years before E.T. tried it! –* **Terry Jones**

Hector's New Trainers
by Amanda Vesey

Poor Hector! All he wants for his birthday is a pair of trainers like everyone else has, the special kind with go-faster stripes, black and blue trim and a football logo on the ankle. But the trainers he gets have a gold star instead of a football logo. How can he ever impress Leroy the school hero, when he's wearing the wrong trainers? But Leroy ends up saving the day – and Hector finds out that sometimes it can be nice to be a little bit different.

I like this book because it shows the shortcomings of 'hero-worship' and 'peer pressure', both of which affect the young and vulnerable
*– **Phil Collins***

from Lottie's Letter
by Gordon Snell

*After finding many injured creatures, Lottie and
Max decide to visit the Queen of the World with
a letter 'signed' by all their animal friends.*

The procession went on till it came to the
Chair in the Air, where the Queen of the
World sat, floating.

She said: 'WISE! WONDERFUL! WELL
DONE! I have never seen a letter with so many
paw-marks, claw-marks, wing-marks, sting-
marks, leg-marks, egg-marks, scale-marks, tail-
marks, tooth-marks and hoof-marks.'

'What will you do?' asked Lottie.

'I shall fly round the world with the letter,'
said the Queen, 'and tell everyone to stop
making such a muck and a muddle and a mess.'

Mother Goose
Comes to Cable Street
by Rosemary Stones and Andrew Mann

*M*other *Goose* *Comes* *to* *Cable* *Street* is a
collection of traditional nursery rhymes,
brought up to date with colourful illustrations
that reflect inner-city life in London.

*This is highly thought-provoking, creative and
superbly illustrated by Dan Jones. It is perfect for
all children in our culturally diverse society. My
children loved it and still do – **Herman Ouseley***

Starting School, Making Friends
Age 5–8

from Peter Pan
by J. M. Barrie

When Peter Pan flies into the home of Wendy, John and Michael, it is only the beginning of their magical adventures in the Neverland. But first of all, they must learn how to fly . . .

Of course Peter had been trifling with them, for no one can fly unless the fairy dust has been blown on him. Fortunately, as we have mentioned, one of his hands was messy with it, and he blew some on each of them, with the most superb results.

'Now just wriggle your shoulders this way,' he said, 'and let go.'

They were all on their beds, and gallant Michael let go first. He did not quite mean to let go, but he did it, and immediately he was borne across the room.

'I flewed!' he screamed while still in mid-air.

John let go and met Wendy near the bathroom.

'Oh, lovely!'

'Oh, ripping!'

'Look at me!'

'Look at me!'

'Look at me!'

They were not nearly so elegant as Peter, they could not help kicking a little, but their heads were bobbing against the ceiling, and there is almost nothing so delicious as that. Peter gave Wendy a hand at first, but had to desist, Tink was so indignant.

Up and down they went, and round and round. Heavenly was Wendy's word.

'I say,' cried John, 'why shouldn't we all go out!'

Of course it was to this that Peter had been luring them.

Michael was ready: he wanted to see how long it took him to do a billion miles. But Wendy hesitated.

'Mermaids!' said Peter again.

'Oo!'

'And there are pirates.'

'Pirates,' cried John, seizing his Sunday hat, 'let us go at once.'

from The Little Mermaid
by Hans Christian Andersen

*The little mermaid lives under the sea in the
kingdom of the Merpeople. She falls in love with
a handsome prince after saving his life and
decides that she must go and seek him out in
the world above the water. So she asks an old
witch for help . . .*

Soon she came to a marshy place where
immense, fat snails were crawling about and in
the middle of it stood a house built of the bones
of unfortunate people who had been ship-
wrecked. Here the witch sat caressing a toad in
the same manner as some people would a pet
bird. She called the ugly fat snails her chickens,
and she let them crawl all over her.

'I know exactly what you are going to ask me,'
said she to the little princess. 'Your wish is
foolish, yet it shall be fulfilled though it is sure
to bring misfortune on you, my fairest princess.
You have come just at the right time,' continued
she; 'had you come after sunset I wouldn't have
been able to help you for another year. You must

swim to land and sit down on the shore and swallow a drink which I will prepare for you. Your tail will then fall and shrink into the things which men call legs. This transformation will be very painful, for you will feel as though a sharp knife passed through your body. All who look on you will say that you are the loveliest child they have ever seen. You will keep all your graceful movements and no dancer will move so lightly. but every step you take will cause you unbearable pain: it will be as though you were walking on the sharp edges of swords and your blood will flow. Can you endure all this suffering? If so, I will grant your request.'

'Yes, I can,' answered the princess, with a faltering voice; for she remembered her dear prince and the immortal soul which her suffering might win.

'Remember,' said the witch, 'that you can never become a mermaid again once you have received human form. You may never return to your sisters and your father's palace and unless you shall win the prince's love to such a degree that he shall leave father and mother for you, that you shall be part of all his thoughts and wishes, and unless the priest join your hands so that you become man and wife, you will never obtain the immortality you seek. Should he marry another you will die on the following day for your heart will break with sorrow and you will be changed to foam on the sea.'

'Still I will do it!' said the little mermaid, pale and trembling as a dying person.

> *This is my favourite children's story because it had an unhappy ending and made me cry. I was tired of princesses and happy endings, and didn't believe in them. I thought of it for the rest of my life, and wrote 'My Love, My Love' because of it*
> *— Rosa Guy*

Top Books

Books by each of these authors were borrowed from libraries by more than a million children during 1995–6:

Janet and Allan Ahlberg
Enid Blyton
Roald Dahl
Goscinny (*Asterix* series)
Dick King-Smith
Ann N. Martin (*The Babysitter's Club* series)
R. L. Stine (*Goosebumps* series)
Kate William (*Sweet Valley High* series)

It Was a Dark and Stormy Night by Janet and Allan Ahlberg was the top-selling fiction title through the Puffin Book Club in 1996–7.

Antonio has been kidnapped by brigands and carried off to their secret cave. To keep them from getting bored, he must tell them a story. But the brigands are hard to please . . .

For the third time, Antonio began his story. 'Right-o! It was a bright and starry night.'

'That's better,' said the chief.

'The silver moon shone down upon the silver beach beside the silver sea.'

'Ah!' sighed the brigands, and one of them – Giorgio – added, 'I love silver.'

'Suddenly, lumbering towards the mighty chief and his brigand band as they sat quietly dozing on the silver sand –'

'That rhymes!' observed the chief, admiringly.

'– came half a dozen hungry bears.'

At once the brigands protested. 'Not bears again!'

'We said no bears!'

'Bears – on a beach? That's silly.'

'All right, then – pirates,' said Antonio. 'Cut-throat pirates charging up across the sand from the left, and South American ruffians –'

'What kind of beach is this?' said the chief.

'– racing in from the right – and massive sharks churning up the waters of the bay, and . . .' Antonio cudgelled his brain for more ideas. 'A crocodile-infested swamp behind them, killer parrots in the palm trees, and . . . and . . .' He paused again to catch his breath and work out, if he could, what happened next.

'What happened next?' said the chief.

(Extract from *It Was a Dark and Stormy Night* by Janet and Allan Ahlberg.)

from Now We Are Six
by A. A. Milne

Waiting at the Window

These are my two drops of rain
Waiting on the window-pane.

I am waiting here to see
Which the winning one will be.

Both of them have different names.
One is John and one is James.

All the best and all the worst
Comes from which of them is first.

James had just begun to ooze.
He's the one I want to lose.

John is waiting to begin.
He's the one I want to win.

James is going slowly on.
Something sort of sticks to John.

John is moving off at last.
James is going pretty fast.

John is rushing down the pane.
James is going slow again.

James has met a sort of smear.
John is getting very near.

Is he going fast enough?
(James has found a piece of fluff.)

John has hurried quickly by.
(James was talking to a fly.)

John is there, and John has won!
Look! I told you! Here's the sun!

---

*One of the most wonderful parts of childhood
is to play imaginary games.* Now We Are Six
conjures up this innocence beautifully
– Carol Vorderman

from The Ugly Duckling
by Hans Christian Andersen

*The ugly duckling has been pecked and teased
since he was born. Always the outsider of the
family, he is laughed at for being large, ugly
and awkward. The poor duckling thinks he will
always be different from the others, until one
day he comes across another kind of bird . . .*

Out of the thicket came three beautiful white
swans. They rustled their wings and swam
lightly down the river. The duckling recognized
them and was seized with a strange sadness.

'I will go up to them, those royal birds,' said
he. 'They will kill me, because I, ugly as I am,
have dared to approach them, but it doesn't
matter. Better be killed by them than be bitten
by the ducks, pecked by the hens, kicked by the
girl who feeds the poultry, and have so much to
suffer during the winter!' He flew into the
water, and swam towards them. They saw him
and swam forward to meet him. 'Only kill me,'
said the poor duckling, and he bowed his head

low, expecting death. But what was this he saw in the clear water? He saw his own reflection – no longer that of a plump, ugly, grey bird, but that of a swan.

It doesn't matter if you are born in a duck-yard when you've been hatched from a swan's egg.

The larger swans swam round him, and stroked him with their beaks, and he was very happy.

Some little children were running about in the garden. They threw grain and bread into the water, and the youngest exclaimed, 'There's a new one!' The others also cried out, 'Yes, a new swan has come!' and they clapped their hands, and ran and told their father and mother. They

threw more bread and cake into the water and everyone said, 'The new one is the best, so young, and so beautiful!' and the old swans bowed before him.

The young swan felt quite ashamed, and hid his head under his wing for he did not know what to do. He was all too happy, but still not proud, for a good heart is never proud.

He remembered how he had been laughed at and cruelly treated; and now he heard everyone say he was the most beautiful of all beautiful birds. The syringa bent down its branches towards him, and the sun shone warmly and brightly. He ruffled his wings, stretched his slender neck, and with joy in his heart said, 'I never dreamed of so much happiness when I was still the Ugly Duckling!'

One of my favourite stories of my childhood is The Ugly Duckling. *I always admired the fact that even though Hans Christian Andersen could not spell his name until well into his twenties, his fairy tales proved that you don't have to be a great writer to be a good story-teller.* The Ugly Duckling *is the classic rags to riches tale told by the master –* **Jeffrey Archer**

from The Wind
in the Willows
by Kenneth Grahame

*Mole is busy doing his spring-cleaning at his
river-bank home when the Water Rat invites
him on a boat trip.*

The Rat sculled smartly across and made fast.
Then he held up his fore-paw as the Mole
stepped gingerly down. 'Lean on that!' he said.
'Now then, step lively!' and the Mole to his
surprise and rapture found himself actually seated
in the stern of a real boat.

'This has been a wonderful day!' said he, as the
Rat shoved off and took to the sculls again. 'Do
you know, I've never been in a boat before in all
my life.'

'What?' cried the Rat, open-mouthed. 'Never
been in a – you never – well, I – what have you
been doing, then?'

'Is it so nice as all that?' asked the Mole shyly,
though he was quite prepared to believe it as he

leant back in his seat and surveyed the cushions, the oars, the rowlocks, and all the fascinating fittings, and felt the boat sway lightly under him.

'Nice? It's the *only* thing,' said the Water Rat solemnly, as he leant forward for his stroke. 'Believe me, my young friend, there is *nothing* – absolutely nothing – half so much worth doing as simply messing about in boats. Simply messing,' he went on dreamily: 'messing – about – in – boats; messing –'

'Look ahead, Rat!' cried the Mole suddenly.

It was too late. The boat struck the bank full tilt. The dreamer, the joyous oarsman, lay on his back at the bottom of the boat, his heels in the air.

'– about in boats – or *with* boats,' the Rat went on composedly, picking himself up with a pleasant laugh. 'In or out of 'em, it doesn't

matter. Nothing seems really to matter, that's the charm of it. Whether you get away, or whether you don't; whether you arrive at your destination or whether you reach somewhere else, or whether you never get anywhere at all, you're always busy, and you never do anything in particular; and when you've done it there's always something else to do, and you can do it if you like, but you'd much better not. Look here! If you've really nothing else on hand this morning, supposing we drop down the river together, and have a long day of it?'

The Mole waggled his toes from sheer happiness, spread his chest with a sigh of full contentment, and leant back blissfully into the soft cushions. '*What* a day I'm having!' he said.

from Nonsense Poems
by Edward Lear

from *The Quangle Wangle's Hat*

I

On the top of the Crumpetty Tree
The Quangle Wangle sat,
But his face you could not see,
On account of his Beaver Hat.
For his Hat was a hundred and two feet wide,
With ribbons and bibbons on every side
And bells, and buttons, and loops, and lace,
So that nobody ever could see the face
Of the Quangle Wangle Quee.

The Quangle Wangle said
To himself on the Crumpetty Tree, –
'Jam; and jelly; and bread;
'Are the best of food for me!
'But the longer I live on this Crumpetty Tree,
'The plainer than ever it seems to me
'That very few people come this way,
'And that life on the whole is far from gay!'
Said the Quangle Wangle Quee.

The Owl and the Pussy-Cat

I

The Owl and the Pussy-Cat went to sea
In a beautiful pea-green boat,
They took some honey, and plenty of money,
Wrapped up in a five-pound note.
The Owl looked up to the stars above,
And sang to a small guitar,
'O lovely Pussy! O Pussy, my love,
'What a beautiful Pussy you are,
'You are,
'You are!
'What a beautiful Pussy you are!'

II

Pussy said to the Owl, 'You elegant fowl!
'How charmingly sweet you sing!
'O let us be married! too long we have tarried:
'But what shall we do for a ring?'
They sailed away for a year and a day,
To the land where the Bong-tree grows,
And there in a wood a Piggy-wig stood,
With a ring at the end of his nose,
His nose,
His nose,
With a ring at the end of his nose.

III

'Dear Pig, are you willing to sell for one shilling
'Your ring?' Said the Piggy, 'I will.'
So they took it away, and were married next
day
By the Turkey who lives on the hill.
They dined on mince, and slices of quince,
Which they ate with a runcible spoon;
And hand in hand, on the edge of the sand,
They danced by the light of the moon,
The moon,
The moon,
They danced by the light of the moon.

This is the poem I most enjoy reading
with my daughter because
1) It is completely mad.
2) It has a lovely rhythm.
3) We can recite it together.
4) It beats being made to re-enact the Famous Five
or Secret Seven by digging tunnels
— Jeremy Paxman

Streaker is no ordinary dog. She's a rocket on four legs, and Trevor has got until the end of the holidays to train her. But Trevor prides himself on his brilliant ideas – one of which is to invent a machine that will give Streaker her daily walk . . .

'Walkies!' I cried and dropped Streaker on to the whirring track.

There was a startled yelp as Streaker was caught by the carpet and hurled backwards at high speed. She shot off the rear of the track, whizzed out through the door, rocketed across the kitchen, and ended up with her backside rammed in the open front of the washing-machine – which luckily wasn't switched on.

Streaker fixed me with a bewildered gaze as if to say, 'How on earth did I get into *this* position?' Her front paws were firmly on the ground, but the back half of her was even more firmly wedged in the washing-machine. I ran

54

over and tried to pull her out as gently as I could, but Streaker was jammed there like King Arthur's sword in the stone.

'Now what?' Tina gave me a silent shrug.

'She can't move,' I went on. 'We've got to get her out. We need help.'

Tina shrugged again. 'What kind of help?' she said. 'Who do we ask? Plumbers? A garage? Fire brigade?'

'Fire brigade!' I leaped to the telephone. 'They get cats out of trees and things, don't they? Maybe they get dogs out of washing-machines.'

(Extract from *The Hundred-Mile-an-Hour Dog* by Jeremy Strong.)

from The Night Before Christmas

by Clement Clarke Moore

'Twas the night before Christmas, when all
  through the house
Not a creature was stirring, not even a mouse:
The stockings were hung by the chimney with
  care,
In hopes that St Nicholas soon would be there;
The children were nestled all snug in their beds
While visions of sugar-plums danced in their
  heads;
And Mamma in her 'kerchief, and I in my cap,
Had just settled down for a long winter's nap,
When out on the lawn there arose such a clatter,
I sprang from my bed to see what was the
  matter,
Away to the window I flew like a flash,
Tore open the shutters and threw up the sash,
The moon on the breast of the new-fallen snow
Gave a lustre of midday to objects below,

When, what to my wondering eyes did appear,
But a miniature sleigh and eight tiny reindeer,
With a little old driver, so lively and quick,
I knew in a moment it must be St Nick,
More rapid than eagles his coursers they came,
And he whistled, and shouted, and called them
    by name:
'Now, Dasher! now, Dancer! now, Prancer and
    Vixen!
On, Comet! on, Cupid! on Donder and Blitzen!
To the top of the porch! to the top of the wall!
Now dash away! dash away! dash away all!'

As dry leaves that before the wild hurricane fly,
When they meet with an obstacle, mount to the
sky,
So up to the housetop the coursers they flew,
With a sleigh full of toys, and St Nicholas too.
And then, in a twinkling, I heard on the roof
The prancing and pawing of each little hoof.
As I drew in my head, and was turning around,
Down the chimney St Nicholas came with a
bound.

> *It's a magical tale which beautifully depicts that gorgeous, happy and cosy scene which we all enjoy on Christmas Eve. Honestly, I'm just an incurable romantic, and possibly a little old-fashioned, even at 27! –* **Toby Anstis**

> *Poetry, fondly remembered and jointly delivered in this case with sound effects, was always a part of my childhood, and in an age of video games has retained its advantage over other distractions with my own kids. No Christmas is complete without a family rendition of this favourite piece –* **Paul Boateng**

Days of Adventure
Age 8-12

from The Lion, the Witch and the Wardrobe
by C. S. Lewis

*Peter, Susan, Edmund and Lucy
accidentally discover the magical land of
Narnia through the back of an old
wardrobe – a land ruled by the cruel
White Witch, where it is always winter.
Only the mysterious Aslan can save the
creatures of Narnia from her spell . . .*

'Who is Aslan?' asked Susan.

'Aslan?' said Mr Beaver. 'Why, don't you know? He's the King. He's the Lord of the whole wood, but not often here, you understand. Never in my time or my father's time. But the word has reached us that he has come back. He is in Narnia at this moment. He'll settle the White Queen all right. It is he, not you, that will save Mr Tumnus.'

'She won't turn him into stone too?' said Edmund.

'Lord love you, Son of Adam, what a simple thing to say!' answered Mr Beaver with a great laugh. 'Turn *him* into stone? If she can stand on her two feet and look him in the face it'll be the most she can do and more than I expect of her. No, no. He'll put all to rights as it says in an old rhyme in these parts:

Wrong will be right, when Aslan comes in sight,
At the sound of his roar, sorrows will be no
    more,
When he bares his teeth, winter meets its death,
And when he shakes his mane, we shall have
    spring again.

You'll understand when you see him.'

'But shall we see him?' asked Susan.

'Why, Daughter of Eve, that's what I brought you here for. I'm to lead you where you shall meet him,' said Mr Beaver.

'Is—is he a man?' asked Lucy.

'Aslan a man!' said Mr Beaver sternly. 'Certainly not. I tell you he is the King of the wood and the son of the great Emperor-beyond-the-Sea. Don't you know who is the King of Beasts? Aslan is a lion – *the* Lion, the great Lion.'

'Ooh!' said Susan, 'I'd thought he was a man.

Is he – quite safe? I shall feel rather nervous about meeting a lion.'

'That you will, dearie, and no mistake,' said Mrs Beaver; 'if there's anyone who can appear before Aslan without their knees knocking, they're either braver than most or else just silly.'

It's pure magic, with such heart. I cried when Aslan dies. I always used to dream of going to Narnia
– Geri Halliwell

The best book I ever read was The Lion, the Witch and the Wardrobe, *when I was ten. I want to read that again now. I love the idea of opening a cupboard door, you step inside, there's a lion and you're being chased through the snow*
– Liam Gallagher

This is my favourite children's book. I was totally engrossed on both occasions I read it
– Peter Mandelson

Just So Stories
by Rudyard Kipling

from *The Cat That Walked By Himself*

Long ago, when all creatures were Wild Things, the Dog, the Horse and the Cow made their first contact with the Man and the Woman. But the elusive Cat was not as easy to bargain with . . .

Cat said, 'I am not a friend, and I am not a servant. I am the Cat who walks by himself, and I wish to come into your Cave.'

Woman said, 'Then why did you not come with First Friend on the first night?'

Cat grew very angry and said, 'Has Wild Dog told tales of me?'

Then the Woman laughed and said, 'You are the Cat who walks by himself, and all places are alike to you. You are neither a friend nor a servant. You have said it yourself. Go away and walk by yourself in all places alike.'

Then Cat pretended to be sorry and said, 'Must I never come into the Cave? Must I never sit by the warm fire? Must I never drink the warm white milk? You are very wise and very beautiful.

You should not be cruel even to a Cat.'

Woman said, 'I knew I was wise, but I did not know I was beautiful. So I will make a bargain with you. If ever I say one word in your praise, you may come into the Cave.'

'And if you say two words in my praise?' said the Cat.

'I never shall,' said the Woman, 'but if I say two words in your praise, you may sit by the fire in the Cave.'

'And if you say three words?' said the Cat.

'I never shall,' said the Woman, 'but if I say three words in your praise, you may drink the warm white milk three times a day for always and always and always.'

Then the Cat arched his back and said, 'Now let the Curtain at the mouth of the Cave, and the Fire at the back of the Cave, and the Milk-pots that stand beside the Fire, remember what my Enemy and the Wife of my Enemy has said.' And he went away through the Wet Wild Woods waving his wild tail and walking by his wild lone.

The Just So Stories are fables for children of all ages. They explain things and make them understandable. As a politician who walks by himself, I read them to this day with the greatest pleasure – **Martin Bell**

from A Thief in the Village
by James Berry

*In the darkness of the night, Nenna and her
brother Man-Man are guarding the coconut
plantation, waiting to catch a thief . . .*

Man-Man and Nenna still stood with four
eyes penetrating all sides of shadows and
plain darkness. It was strange how after a long
time in darkness they got to seeing better.

Unexpectedly Man-Man said, 'Did you hear
that?'

Excitement electrified Nenna. 'No. Wha' was
it?'

Man-Man whispered, 'Footsteps . . . A twig
did snap.'

Their breath stopped. They listened.

'You hear it again?'

Man-Man waited. Then his voice barely
carried. 'No.'

Unbelievable, from a tree next to them, a bunch
of coconuts of perhaps ten or twelve dropped and
broke loose like a great pile of huge stones. A blast
of gun deafened Nenna. Then panic!

A dim figure slid down smooth palm trunk like a man cut loose down a grease pole. And a flight now! All wild and crazy and mad! A tearing through scattered undergrowth like a mad wild horse. Another frightening gun blast! The figure fell with a terrible splash into the old irrigation canal, where there were few banana trees. It retrieved itself like a miracle and took off again with swift force. Racing feet thudded down, pounding through coconut-field darkness, swinging back some shrub branches. And, no holding them, Man-Man and Nenna raced behind hollering, 'Thief! Stop thief! Stop thief!'

They seemed to be getting closer. Then at the wire fence they heard the loud ripping cry of clothes torn. Then again the swift pounding feet raced away, along a narrow track on the adjoining land. And suddenly it was just Man-Man and Nenna panting their guts out.

'When – when he slide down the tree,' Nenna panted, 'I did t'ink he really dead.'

Her brother hissed with a wheezy giggle. And both collapsed, laughing helplessly.

I like this book because it is about Jamaica now *not just Jamaica 'once upon a time'. And because it shows that the colours and rhythm and spirit of real children are as exciting as any fairy tale –* **Angie Le Mar**

Top Books

The BBC's 'Bookworm' and Waterstone's poll of 1997 showed that the nation's favourite children's book was *Matilda* by Roald Dahl.

1 *Matilda* – Roald Dahl

2 *The Wind in the Willows* – Kenneth Grahame

3 *The Lion, the Witch and the Wardrobe* – C. S. Lewis

4 *Winnie-the-Pooh* – A. A. Milne

5 *The Hobbit* – J. R. R. Tolkien

6 *Charlie and the Chocolate Factory* – Roald Dahl

7 *Swallows and Amazons* – Arthur Ransome

8 *The BFG* – Roald Dahl

9 *Alice's Adventures in Wonderland* – Lewis Carroll

10 *The Secret Garden* – Frances Hodgson Burnett

Matilda is an exceptional
girl, but her parents think she is
just a nuisance. When one day she
is attacked by her odious
headmistress, Matilda suddenly
discovers she has a remarkable
power to avenge herself!

The Trunchbull was sitting behind the teacher's table staring with a mixture of horror and fascination at the newt wriggling in the glass. Matilda's eyes were also riveted on the glass. And now, quite slowly, there began to creep over Matilda a most extraordinary and peculiar feeling. The feeling was mostly in the eyes. A kind of electricity seemed to be gathering inside them. A sense of power was brewing in those eyes of hers, a feeling of great strength was settling itself deep inside her eyes. But there was also another feeling which was something else altogether, and which she could not understand. It was like flashes of lightning. Little waves of lightning seemed to be flashing out of her eyes. Her eyeballs were beginning to get hot, as though vast energy was building up somewhere inside them. It was an amazing sensation. She kept her eyes steadily on the glass, and now the power was concentrating itself in one small part of each eye and growing stronger and stronger and it felt as though millions of tiny little invisible arms with hands on them were shooting out of her eyes towards the glass she was staring at.

'*Tip it!*' Matilda whispered. '*Tip it over!*'

(Extract from *Matilda* by Roald Dahl.)

from Alice's Adventures in Wonderland
by Lewis Carroll

*When Alice falls down a rabbit hole she
finds herself in the bizarre world of Wonderland –
where she meets some very strange creatures and
finds out that nothing is quite what it seems . . .*

'In *that* direction,' the Cat said, waving its right
paw round, 'lives a Hatter: and in *that*
direction,' waving the other paw, 'lives a March
Hare. Visit either you like: they're both mad.'

'But I don't want to go among mad people,'
Alice remarked.

'Oh, you can't help that,' said the Cat: 'we're
all mad here. I'm mad. You're mad.'

'How do you know I'm mad?' said Alice.

'You must be,' said the Cat, 'or you wouldn't
have come here.'

Alice didn't think that proved it at all;
however, she went on, 'And how do you know
that you're mad?'

'To begin with,' said the Cat, 'a dog's not mad. You grant that?'

'I suppose so,' said Alice.

'Well, then,' the Cat went on, 'you see, a dog growls when it's angry, and wags its tail when it's pleased. Now *I* growl when I'm pleased, and wag my tail when I'm angry. Therefore I'm mad.'

'*I* call it purring, not growling,' said Alice.

'Call it what you like,' said the Cat. 'Do you play croquet with the Queen to-day?'

'I should like it very much,' said Alice, 'but I haven't been invited yet.'

'You'll see me there,' said the Cat, and vanished.

Alice was not much surprised at this, she was getting so used to queer things happening. While she was looking at the place where it had been, it suddenly appeared again.

'By-the-bye, what became of the baby?' said the Cat. 'I'd nearly forgotten to ask.'

'It turned into a pig,' Alice quietly said, just as if it had come back in a natural way.

'I thought it would,' said the Cat, and vanished again.

A really good children's book is one that gives you as much pleasure as an adult as it did when you were a child. 'Alice' is such a book
– Russell Stannard

from Cautionary Tales
for Children
by Hilaire Belloc

Matilda

WHO TOLD LIES, AND WAS
BURNED TO DEATH

Matilda told such Dreadful Lies,
    It made one Gasp and Stretch one's Eyes;
Her Aunt, who, from her Earliest Youth,
Had kept a Strict Regard for Truth,
Attempted to Believe Matilda:
The effort very nearly killed her,
And would have done so, had not She
Discovered this Infirmity
For once, towards the Close of Day,
Matilda, growing tired of play,
And finding she was left alone,
Went tiptoe to the Telephone
And summoned the Immediate Aid
Of London's Noble Fire-Brigade.
Within an hour the Gallant Band
Were pouring in on every hand,

From Putney, Hackney Downs and Bow,
With Courage high and Hearts a-glow
They galloped, roaring through the Town,
'Matilda's House is Burning Down!'
Inspired by British Cheers and Loud
Proceeding from the Frenzied Crowd,
They ran their ladders through a score
Of windows on the Ball Room Floor;
And took Peculiar Pains to Souse
The Pictures up and down the House,
Until Matilda's Aunt succeeded
In showing them they were not needed
And even then she had to pay
To get the Men to go away!

It happened that a few Weeks later
Her Aunt was off to the Theatre
To see that Interesting Play
The Second Mrs Tanqueray.
She had refused to take her Niece
To hear this Entertaining Piece:
A Deprivation Just and Wise
To Punish her for Telling Lies.
That Night a Fire *did* break out –
You should have heard Matilda Shout!
You should have heard her Scream and Bawl,
And throw the window up and call
To People passing in the Street –
(The rapidly increasing Heat

Encouraging her to obtain
Their confidence) – but all in vain!
For every time She shouted 'Fire!'
They only answered 'Little Liar!'
And therefore when her Aunt returned,
Matilda, and the House, were Burned.

The perfect length for reading at bedtime;
enjoyable for both parent and child; we liked it so
much we called our third child after it
– Robert Harris

from The Little Prince
by Antoine de Saint-Exupéry

Once when I was six years old I saw a magnificent picture in a book called *True Stories of the Virgin Forest*. It showed a boa constrictor swallowing a wild beast. Here is a copy of the drawing.

In the book it said: 'Boa constrictors swallow their prey whole, without chewing. Afterwards they are unable to move, and they digest by going to sleep for six months.'

This made me think a lot about the adventures of the jungle and, eventually, I succeeded with a coloured pencil in making my first drawing. My Drawing Number One. It looked like this:

I showed my masterpiece to the grown-ups, and asked if my drawing frightened them.

'Why would a hat frighten anyone?' they answered.

My drawing was not of a hat. It was of a boa constrictor digesting an elephant. So then I drew the inside of the boa constrictor, for the benefit of the grown-ups. (Grown-ups always need explanations.) My Drawing Number Two looked like this:

The grown-ups now advised me to give up drawing boa constrictors altogether, from the inside or the outside, and devote myself instead to geography, history, arithmetic and grammar. So it was that, at the age of six, I gave up a wonderful career as a painter. I had been discouraged by the failure of my Drawing Number One and my Drawing Number Two. Grown-ups never understand anything by themselves, and it is exhausting for children always and forever to be giving explanations.

It's all about a little boy dealing with very adult issues which are represented by different characters e.g. The Fox, The Rose and The Mathematician. He goes in search of something new and finds he is happiest where he was when he started
– Mark Owen

It is a book that transcends any age of the reader with its magical depth and charming illustrations. We all grow to know foxes, hunters and businessmen, if we are lucky some of us find roses to care for. I haven't the funky flares but I'd like to think I have a trace of the Little Prince in my heart **– Chris Packham**

Ruby and Garnet are ten-year-old identical twins who do everything together, especially since their mother died three years earlier. Their 'double act' certainly spooks Rose, the new woman in their dad's life. But can it last for ever?

Garnet and I have this special language. We've got heaps of made-up words for things. Sometimes we don't use words at all, we use signs. Little tiny things like widening our eyes or putting our heads slightly to one side. We signal to each other and then both start up a pretend coughing fit or sneeze simultaneously or shriek with manic laughter.

Rose isn't used to this. It doesn't half make her jump.

'Pack it in,' says Dad.

I glance at Garnet.

'Pack it in what, Dad?' we say simultaneously.

'Less of the cheek,' says Dad, taking one hand off the steering wheel and swatting at us.

'How do they do that?' Rose asks.

'How do we *do* what?' we say.

'Stop it! You're giving me the creeps. Can you really read each other's thoughts?' she says, shivering.

'Of course they can't,' says Dad.

'Then how can they say the same thing at the same time in that weird way?' Rose says, peering at us.

'I don't know,' says Dad, shrugging.

'*We* know,' we say, and we raise our eyebrows and make our eyes glitter in a mysterious and mystic manner.

(Extract from *Double Act* by Jacqueline Wilson.)

from Professor Branestawm's Dictionary
by Norman Hunter

Professor Branestawm is the master of inventions and contraptions. He's also managed to invent a whole new list of meanings for everyday words. Here are some examples:

A

Aaron. What a wig has.

abandon. What a hat has.

abate. Something for catching fish.

abominable. A piece of explosive swallowed by a male cow.

abundance. A waltz for cakes.

ABUNDANCE

accident. Mark made by a chopper.
account. A countess's husband.
accountant. Insect who is good at figures.

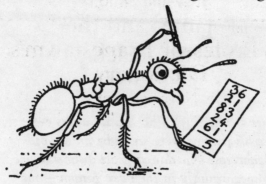

acquire. Group of singers.
addition. What a dinner table has.
allocate. A greeting for Catherine.
allotment. A good deal is intended.
also. Everybody stitch.
analyse. Ann doesn't tell the truth.

from James and the Giant Peach
by Roald Dahl

James has lived with his beastly aunts ever since his parents were eaten by an escaped rhinoceros. One day, a peach begins to grow spectacularly in the back garden – and nobody yet realizes how it is going to change James's life . . .

The two women and the small boy stood absolutely still on the grass underneath the tree, gazing up at this extraordinary fruit. James's little face was glowing with excitement, his eyes were as big and bright as two stars. He could see the peach swelling larger and larger as clearly as if it were a balloon being blown up.

In half a minute, it was the size of a melon!

In another half-minute, it was *twice* as big again!

'Just *look* at it growing!' Aunt Spiker cried.

'Will it ever stop!' Aunt Sponge shouted,

waving her fat arms and starting to dance around in circles.

And now it was so big it looked like an enormous butter-coloured pumpkin dangling from the top of the tree.

'Get away from that tree trunk, you stupid boy!' Aunt Spiker yelled. 'The slightest shake and I'm sure it'll fall off! It must weigh twenty or thirty pounds at least!'

The branch that the peach was growing upon was beginning to bend over further and further because of the weight.

'Stand back!' Aunt Sponge shouted. 'It's coming down! The branch is going to break!'

This is my favourite children's book. James's spirit to survive against all adversity with his carefully chosen bunch of friends has been an inspiration to me during many moments of my adult life
– Liccy Dahl

from Coming to England
by Floella Benjamin

*When the young Floella Benjamin first arrived
in England, not only had she come all the way
from Trinidad, she had not seen her parents for
fifteen months. But there, waiting for the ship,
was her 'Marmie' . . .*

At long last the ship appeared to be getting closer to the quay. I could see hundreds of faces looking up at us, trying to spot their loved ones. I looked desperately for Marmie, hoping I would recognize her lovely face among the crowd. Suddenly there she was, beaming with joy like an angel, waving frantically at us. She clutched her bosom and seemed to shake her head with a sigh of relief as if to say 'thank goodness my children are safe'. Then she started to wipe away tears with her handkerchief and motioned us to stay where we were, which was not really a problem as the four of us couldn't move – we were too numbed with excitement.

There was a man beside her who was not my father. I could see her talking to him and pointing us out. Eventually, when the ship was anchored, he came on board up the gangway. He made his way over to us and introduced himself. He was a social worker whose job it was to meet passengers as they arrived and help those who needed advice about how to get to their new destination. Not everyone had friends or family to meet them on arrival so the social worker was essential. He looked after us because Marmie was not allowed to come on board and as we were children travelling alone he took charge of us. He bundled all our luggage together and swiftly pushed past the other passengers, the four of us in tow behind him. My heart pounded loudly like thunder as I climbed down the gangplank, this time not with fear but with joy as I ran towards Marmie.

We all made a dash for her and hugged her. She squeezed us so tightly I felt I would break. The love and joy that passed through every bit of our bodies was overwhelming. I was at last in paradise, clutching Marmie. I never wanted to be away from her again. When we finally broke loose from her she opened a bag and took out something for each of us. 'I thought you might be a little cold,' she said, 'so I got these for you.' She handed me a powder-blue knitted Marks & Spencer's button-fronted cardigan, embroidered with pink and yellow flowers. It was gorgeous; I adored it, my first English present. I squeezed it affectionately. I felt as if I had been sprinkled with magic dust and that all my dreams were coming true. I was back with my beloved Marmie at long last.

It may sound vain, but my children love to hear the stories of my early life and about their roots, which seem to have made a lot of difference to their lives – **Floella Benjamin**

from The Enchanted Castle
by E. Nesbit

*Gerald, Cathy and Jimmy discover a ring that
has special, but very unpredictable, powers. One
day they decide to make a group of 'Ugly-
Wuglies' from household objects, who are to be
the audience for their play. But, due to the ring,
the children's performance of* Beauty and the
Beast *has some very strange consequences . . .*

'I wish,' said Mabel, taking on herself the
weight of the tea-urn, 'I wish those creatures
we made were alive. We should get something
like applause then.'

'I'm jolly glad they aren't,' said Gerald,
arranging the baize and the towel-horse. 'Brutes!
It makes me feel quite silly when I catch their
paper eyes.'

The curtains were drawn back. There lay the
hearthrug-coated beast, in flat abandonment
among the tropic beauties of the garden, the
pampas-grass shrubbery, the indiarubber plant
bushes, the geranium-trees and the urn
fountain. Beauty was ready to make her great

89

entry in all the thrilling splendour of despair.
And then suddenly it all happened.

Mademoiselle began it: she applauded the
garden scene – with hurried little clappings of
her quick French hands. Eliza's fat red palms
followed heavily, and then – someone else was
clapping, six or seven people, and their clapping
made a dull padded sound. Nine faces instead of

two were turned towards the stage, and seven out of the nine were painted, pointed paper faces. And every hand and every face was alive. The applause grew louder as Mabel glided forward, and as she paused and looked at the audience her unstudied pose of horror and amazement drew forth applause louder still; but it was not loud enough to drown the shrieks of Mademoiselle and Eliza as they rushed from the room, knocking chairs over and crushing each other in the doorway. Two distant doors banged, Mademoiselle's door and Eliza's door.

'Curtain! curtain! quick!' cried Beauty-Mabel, in a voice that wasn't Mabel's or the Beauty's. 'Jerry – those things *have* come alive. Oh, whatever *shall* we do?'

I can still remember – over fifty years later – my feeling of thrill and chill when the Ugly-Wuglies come alive and start clapping . . . a seminal moment for me as a mystery writer
*– **Antonia Fraser***

---

*No other children except Natalie seem to want to be
with Tulip. And so begins a strange friendship . . .*

And I saw lots of her at school. She had no
other friends. Nobody else could stand the
embarrassment of pretending that they believed
her awful lies.

'The army's borrowing one of our fields today.
When I get home, they're going to let me drive
a tank.'

'Oh, I really believe that, Tulip!'

'So likely!'

They'd walk off, scoffing. I'd stare at the
ground, and, guess what, I'd feel *sorry* for her. I
knew she was making a fool of me in front of
everyone. (Only an idiot would make a show of
believing her rubbish.) But instead of just
walking away, exasperated, like everyone else,
I'd try taking her arm and distracting her.

'Want to play *Road of Bones* on the way home?'

She'd shake me off, rude and ungrateful. Even
back then I had to ask myself why I stayed

around. It wasn't out of pity, I knew that. Nobody *has* to carry on telling ridiculous lies, even after it's obvious that no one believes them.

'I've won a big competition. I found a scratchcard in my cornflakes and I was lucky. So now I've won this beautiful yellow silk dress.'

Next time we bought sweets in Harry's supermarket, I'd linger by the breakfast cereal shelves.

'There's nothing about a competition on any of these packets.'

'No. It was a scratchcard inside.'

'Strange that no one else got one.'

'They only sent out a few as a special anniversary thing. That's why the prize is a yellow silk dress. It's the very same one that the model wore in their first advert.'

That's what Dad came to call the Tulip touch – that tiny detail that almost made you wonder if she might, just for once, be telling the truth.

(Extract from *The Tulip Touch* by Anne Fine.)

from Rip Van Winkle
by Washington Irving

*Rip Van Winkle falls asleep one night in the
mysterious Kaatskill Mountains. On returning to
his town he finds his house empty and the local
people unfamiliar. He thinks he must be losing
his mind, until he sees a face he thinks
he recognizes . . .*

The name of the child, the air of the mother,
the tone of her voice, all awakened a train of
recollections in his mind. 'What is your name, my
good woman?' asked he.

'Judith Gardenier.'

'And your father's name?'

'Ah, poor man, Rip Van Winkle was his name,
but it's twenty years since he went away from
home with his gun, and never has been heard of
since – his dog came home without him; but
whether he shot himself, or was carried away by
the Indians, nobody can tell. I was then but a
little girl.'

Rip had but one question more to ask; but he
put it with a faltering voice:

'Where's your mother?'

'Oh, she too had died but a short time since; she broke a blood vessel in a fit of passion, at a New England pedlar.'

There was a drop of comfort, at least, in this intelligence. The honest man could contain himself no longer. He caught his daughter and her child in his arms. 'I am your father!' cried he. 'Young Rip Van Winkle once – old Rip Van Winkle now! Does nobody know poor Rip Van Winkle?'

All stood amazed, until an old woman, tottering out from among the crowd, put her hand to her brow and, peering under it in his face for a moment, exclaimed, 'Sure enough! It is Rip Van Winkle – it is himself! Welcome home again, old neighbour. Why, where have you been these twenty long years?'

Time is the final frontier, not space – it fascinates me. Rip Van Winkle *was the first story that made me realize you could bend time by using your imagination* – **Sam McBratney**

from Little Women
by Louisa May Alcott

*It is the time of the American Civil War
and the four March sisters have to
struggle to make ends meet and to keep
up their spirits.*

'Christmas won't be Christmas without any presents,' grumbled Jo, lying on the rug.

'It's so dreadful to be poor!' sighed Meg, looking down at her old dress.

'I don't think it's fair for some girls to have plenty of pretty things, and other girls nothing at all,' added little Amy, with an injured sniff.

'We've got father and mother and each other,' said Beth contentedly, from her corner.

The four young faces on which the firelight shone brightened at the cheerful words, but darkened again as Jo said sadly, –

'We haven't got father, and shall not have him for a long time.' She didn't say 'perhaps never,' but each silently added it, thinking of father far away, where the fighting was.

Nobody spoke for a minute; then Meg said in an altered tone,–

'You know the reason mother proposed not having any presents this Christmas was because it is going to be a hard winter for every one; and she thinks we ought not to spend money for pleasure, when our men are suffering so in the army. We can't do much, but we can make our little sacrifices, and ought to do it gladly. But I am afraid I don't;' and Meg shook her head, as she thought regretfully of all the pretty things she wanted.

It was a major part of my growing up. I read and re-read it over again and was intrigued by the March family – I loved the characters. I cried and cried over it, to the amusement of my family, and watched it faithfully on a Sunday when it was made into a television series – **Gloria Hunniford**

from The Silver Sword
by Ian Serraillier

This is the story of four children's struggle to stay alive throughout the years of Nazi occupation in Poland, and is based on a real-life account.

'Don't stand there staring at me, little girl,' said the burly sentry who was on duty.

'I'm not a little girl. I'll be eighteen next week,' said Ruth. 'And I want to see your officer.'

'The whole of Warsaw wants to see my officer. Run away and play.'

'It's very important.'

'Run away.'

Ruth was angry. 'It's all right for you. You've got plenty to eat and drink and warm clothes, too, and a bed to sleep in. Didn't you come here to set us free? You must let me see your officer.'

The sentry grinned. 'Well, seeing it's your birthday next week, I might stretch a point. But I don't hold out much hope that he'll see you.'

He disappeared inside the post.

A moment later he came out.

'The lieutenant says come back the year after

next,' said the sentry.

But before he realized what had happened, Ruth had pushed past him and into the post.

A worried-looking lieutenant was sitting at a desk, typing.

'Hey, you young hussy, come out!' cried the sentry.

'Leave her to me, Ivan,' said the lieutenant, and Ivan went out, swearing under his breath.

'You're a determined young lady,' said the lieutenant.

'I'm not a little girl, anyway,' said Ruth.

'What is it you want?'

'I want food and clothes and blankets, pencils and as much paper as you can spare. I've got sixteen children –'

The lieutenant gasped and nearly fell into the waste-paper basket.

'Seventeen, if you count the one that's lost. He really is mine – he's my brother, Edek. So is my sister, Bronia. The others are just my school. They're all half starving and they're keen to learn and they've got nothing to write on.'

*This is my favourite book from my schooldays. We used to read it out loud in class and I really liked doing all the foreign accents – **Jarvis Cocker***

Lousy Legends

Poets were highly respected in the Celt world – like pop singers today. And, like pop singers, they were well paid. The bad news is that it was a long hard job to train as a Celtic poet. A pop singer probably trains for 12 whole minutes – a Celtic poet trained for 12 years.

Poets learned grammar and very long poems – 80 in the first six years. They learned another 95 in the next three years, and by the end of the 12 years' training they would know 350 story-poems . . . if they survived, that is.

Because learning a story-poem an hour or so long took a lot of concentration. Have you ever had a teacher complain that you lack concentration? Did they nag you into concentrating? Think yourself lucky – you could have had a Celtic poetry teacher.

(Extract from *Horrible Histories: The Cut-Throat Celts* by Terry Deary.)

Top ten bestsellers at School Book Fairs during 1997:

1 *Goosebumps* series
2 *Teletubbies* series
3 Spice Girls titles
4 *The Invisible Dog* – Dick King-Smith
5 *Star Wars* titles
6 *Horrible Histories* series
7 *The BFG* – Roald Dahl
8 *Animal Ark: Fox in the Frost* – Lucy Daniels
9 *Matilda* – Roald Dahl
10 *Animal Stories* – Dick King-Smith

The Listeners
by Walter de la Mare

'Is there anybody there?' said the Traveller,
    Knocking on the moonlit door;
And his horse in the silence champed the grasses
    Of the forest's ferny floor:
And a bird flew up out of the turret,
    Above the Traveller's head:
And he smote upon the door again a second
        time;
    'Is there anybody there?' he said.
But no one descended to the Traveller;
    No head from the leaf-fringed sill
Leaned over and looked into his grey eyes,
    Where he stood perplexed and still.
But only a host of phantom listeners
    That dwelt in the lone house then
Stood listening in the quiet of the moonlight
    To that voice from the world of men:
Stood thronging the faint moonbeams on the
        dark stair
    That goes down to the empty hall,
Hearkening in an air stirred and shaken
    By the lonely Traveller's call.

And he felt in his heart their strangeness,
    Their stillness answering his cry,
While his horse moved, cropping the dark turf,
    'Neath the starred and leafy sky;
For he suddenly smote on the door, even
    Louder, and lifted his head: –
'Tell them I came, and no one answered,
    That I kept my word,' he said.
Never the least stir made the listeners,
    Though every word he spake
Fell echoing through the shadowiness of the still
       house

From the one man left awake:
Ay, they heard his foot upon the stirrup,
    And the sound of iron on stone,
And how the silence surged softly backward,
    When the plunging hoofs were gone.

> *I remember this poem held and gripped me
> when I was a youngster — and still does. It
> encaptures that most precious of qualities for a
> poem, the gift of discovering something truly
> wonderful — the created fantasies stir and twist
> the imagination. The pictures made by the poet
> will last for ever in the reader's mind, and that
> makes this poem the work of a writer of
> true quality* — **Gerald Seymour**

from An Enemy at Green Knowe
by Lucy M. Boston

Tolly and his friend Ping are staying at the mysterious house of Green Knowe, where strange things always seem to happen. Like the mirror which doesn't reflect what it should . . .

'All I can think,' said Ping at last, 'is that this glass reflects the right place but at another time.'

'It only reflects the ceiling half of the room where nothing goes on, so it could be ages before anyone noticed,' Tolly agreed.

'The question is, does it reflect the past or the future?'

'It will be the past, in this house.'

'Lift it down, Tolly, and let's look at it properly.'

They lifted it down and propped it on a chair seat, kneeling down to look in it. It showed their two interested faces cheek by cheek and their arms round each other's shoulders, and that filled up the whole surface.

'Well, that's now at any rate,' said Tolly.

'How do you know? It may be the next time we look in it.'

'Mirror, mirror, on the wall,
Who is the cleverest of us all?'

sang Tolly, teasingly pushing Ping over. Their mock fight ended with their tumbling one at each side of the mirror. From there, each boy saw in it a woman's face. It was colourless, and like a sculptured saint's head on a cathedral porch. But this face had an evil sneer, as shocking as if the expression of one of the gargoyles had strayed on to the face of the Madonna. It was there for so short a time they were left wondering if they had imagined it. Of course they looked round the room. There were two sculptured heads behind them on the Norman fireplace, but not at all like the one they had seen. These were restful and gravely smiling.

'Lordy!' said Tolly, sitting down with a bump. 'To think I said I liked ghosts!

*This book is kindling for the imagination: a battle of magic, ghosts, a murderous witch — even a wicked old alchemist. What more could I have wanted? – **Robin Jarvis***

from Treasure Island
by Robert Louis Stevenson

*Having discovered a map showing the
location of hidden treasure, the crew of the
Hispaniola are on their way to find it. But
young Jim Hawkins, concealed in an apple
barrel, overhears Long John Silver and
his comrades making treacherous plans
for the rest of the crew . . .*

'Right you are,' said Silver, 'rough and ready. But mark you here: I'm an easy man – I'm quite the gentleman, says you; but this time it's serious. Dooty is dooty mates. I give my vote – death. When I'm in Parlyment, and riding in my coach, I don't want none of these sea-lawyers in the cabin a-coming home, unlooked for, like the devil at prayers. Wait is what I say; but when the time comes, why let her rip!'

'John,' cries the coxswain, 'you're a man!'

'You'll say so, Israel, when you see,' said Silver. 'Only one thing I claim – I claim Trelawney. I'll wring his calf's head off his body with these hands. Dick!' he added, breaking off, 'you just jump up, like a sweet lad, and get me an apple, to wet my pipe like.'

You may fancy the terror I was in! I should have leaped out and run for it, if I had found the strength; but my limbs and heart alike misgave me. I heard Dick begin to rise, and then someone seemingly stopped him, and the voice of Hands exclaimed:

'Oh, stow that! Don't you get sucking of that bilge, John. Let's have a go of the rum.'

'Dick,' said Silver, 'I trust you. I've a gauge on the keg, mind. There's the key; you fill a pannikin and bring it up.'

Terrified as I was, I could not help thinking to myself that this must have been how Mr Arrow got the strong waters that destroyed him.

Dick was gone but a little while, and during his absence Israel spoke straight on in the cook's ear. It was but a word or two that I could catch, and yet I gathered some important news; for, besides other scraps that tended to the same purpose, this whole clause was audible: 'Not another man of them'll jine.' Hence there were still faithful men on board.

When Dick returned, one after another of the trio took the pannikin and drank – one 'To luck'; another with a 'Here's to old Flint'; and Silver himself saying, in a kind of song, 'Here's to ourselves, and hold your luff, plenty of prizes and plenty of duff.'

Just then a sort of brightness fell upon me in the barrel, and, looking up, I found the moon had risen, and was silvering the mizzen-top and shining white on the luff of the foresail; and almost at the same time the voice of the look-out shouted 'Land ho!'

> *I enjoyed it because as a young boy growing up in the docks in Glasgow seeing the large ships, I used to think about the book* Treasure Island, *which was a wonderful story. It offered excitement and adventure and was definitely one of my favourites* – **Alex Ferguson**

> *Okay, it's an obvious choice, but there are reasons why classics are classics. Character, plot, adventure, suspense, humour and writing of a kind that should make any living writer blush – **Stephen Fry***

> **Treasure Island** *is simply the most enjoyable adventure story ever written – pirates, treasure, Blind Pew's stick tap-tapping – a great book, to be read in or out of an apple barrel*
> **– Martin Waddell**

from The Phoenix and
the Carpet
by E. Nesbit

*When Robert, Anthea, Jane and Cyril have a
new carpet laid in their nursery, a very
mysterious egg rolls out. And when the children
accidentally knock the egg into the fire, it
hatches — and a Phoenix appears . . .*

'It's only a very little scorched,' said the
Phoenix, apologetically; 'it will come out in
the wash. Please go on reading.'

The children gathered round the table.

'The size of an eagle,' Cyril went on, 'its head
finely crested with a beautiful plumage, its neck
covered with feathers of a gold colour, and the
rest of its body purple; only the tail white, and
the eyes sparkling like stars. They say that it lives
about five hundred years in the wilderness, and
when advanced in age it builds itself a pile of
sweet wood and aromatic gums, fires it with the
wafting of its wings, and thus burns itself; and
that from its ashes arises a worm, which in

111

time grows up to be a Phoenix. Hence the Phoenicians gave –'

'Never mind what they gave,' said the Phoenix, ruffling its golden feathers. 'They never gave much, anyway; they always were people who gave nothing for nothing. That book ought to be destroyed. It's most inaccurate. The rest of my body was *never* purple, and as for my tail – well, I simply ask you, is it white?'

It turned round and gravely presented its golden tail to the children.

'No, it's not,' said everybody.

'No, and it never was,' said the Phoenix. 'And that about the worm is just a vulgar insult. The Phoenix has an egg, like all respectable birds. It makes a pile – that part's all right – and it lays its egg, and it burns itself; and it goes to sleep and wakes up in its egg, and comes out and goes on living again, and so on for ever and ever. I can't tell you how weary I got of it – a restless existence; no repose.'

'But how did your egg get *here*?' asked Anthea.

'Ah, that's my life-secret,' said the Phoenix. 'I couldn't tell it to any one who wasn't really sympathetic. I've always been a misunderstood bird. You can tell that by what they say about the worm. I might tell *you*,' it went on, looking at Robert with eyes that were indeed starry. '*You* put me on the fire –'

Robert looked uncomfortable.

'The rest of us made the fire of sweet-scented woods and gums, though,' said Cyril.

'And – and it was an accident my putting you on the fire,' said Robert, telling thc truth with some difficulty, for he did not know how the Phoenix might take it. It took it in the most unexpected manner.

'Your candid avowal,' it said, 'removes my last scruple. I will tell you my story.'

'And you won't vanish, or anything sudden will you?' asked Anthea, anxiously.

'Why?' it asked, puffing out the golden feathers, 'do you wish me to stay here?'

'Oh *yes*,' said every one, with unmistakable sincerity.

'Why?' asked the Phoenix again, looking modestly at the tablecloth.

'Because,' said every one at once, and then stopped short; only Jane added after a pause, 'you are the most beautiful person we've ever seen.'

Greg took a deep breath and glanced up to the patio. Mrs Walker had covered her face with her hands. Her husband was leaning over her, trying to comfort her.

'Well . . .' Greg started.

'Go ahead, son,' Riddick urged softly. 'Do you know where Shari is?'

'It's the camera,' Greg blurted out. He could suddenly feel the blood throbbing against his temples.

He took a deep breath and then continued. 'You see, this camera is weird.'

'What do you mean?' Riddick asked quietly.

Greg took another deep breath. 'I took Shari's photograph. Before. When I first arrived. I took two photos. And she was invisible. In both of them. See?'

Riddick closed his eyes, then opened them. 'No. I don't understand.'

'Shari was invisible in the photo. Everything else was there. But she wasn't. She had vanished, see. And then, later, she vanished for real. The camera – it predicts the future, I think. Or it makes bad things happen.' Greg raised the camera, attempting to hand it to the policeman.

Riddick made no attempt to take it. He just stared hard at Greg, his eyes narrowing, his expression hardening.

Greg felt a sudden stab of fear.

Oh, no, he thought. Why is he looking at me like that?

What is he going to do?

(Extract from *Say Cheese and Die!* by R. L. Stine.)

W. H. Smith's top-selling titles April–Sept 1997 were all from the series *Goosebumps*:

1 *Night of the Living Dummy*
2 *How I Got My Shrunken Head*
3 *The Headless Ghost*
4 *Welcome to Dead House*
5 *Egg Monsters from Mars*

```
┌─────────────────────────────────────┐
│            Chosen by                  │
│    Thelma Barlow (Mavis Wilton        │
│        in 'Coronation Street')        │
└─────────────────────────────────────┘
```

from The Kelpie's Pearls
by Mollie Hunter

*Morag MacLeod lives alone in the wild Scottish
Highlands. Although her house looks down upon
the loch, she has never seen the Loch Ness
Monster. But when she meets the Kelpie, or
water sprite, it seems he can make her wish
come true . . .*

It was in this path of sunlight that the monster
appeared. One moment there was nothing but
the blank gold of the ripples dancing, and the
next, there was a dark spot among them. The
dark spot rose above the water; three more dark
patches appeared in line with it among the
ripples. From the crowd there came a long
sighing sound and somewhere among them a
child's voice shrieked, *'The Monster!'*

Morag sat watching it, entranced. It began to
move in an easterly direction raising a great
flurry of water behind it, its head swaying and
the humps behind it rising and falling the way a

snake's body does. Then it turned inshore and began to swim in a diagonal line to where Morag was sitting. It came to within thirty yards of her. She could see it clearly – the long neck, the short blunt head, the wide mouth. The sun struck sparkles of light from the greyish humps of its back and she thought, 'It must be scales like a fish that's on it, surely, to make it sparkle so.'

Then the monster altered course till it was swimming west, parallel with the edge of the loch. Now it looked black against the sun. It dived. Morag scanned the blank surface of the loch. The crowd murmured with disappointment, then they roared as it surfaced again a hundred yards out. The head and one of the humps showed above the surface for a moment, then they disappeared and there was only the dark blue water with the sunlight trail fading from it and the gulls dipping and gliding above it.

from The Story of
Doctor Dolittle
by Hugh Lofting

*Doctor Dolittle fills his house with so many
animals that he drives his patients away. Among
the creatures is the very rare pushmi-pullyu.*

No matter which way you came towards it, it
was always facing you. And besides, only one
half of it slept at a time. The other head was
always awake – and watching. This was why they
were never caught and never seen in zoos.
Though many of the greatest hunters and the
cleverest zookeepers spent years of their lives
searching through the jungles in all weather for
pushmi-pullyus, not a single one had ever been
caught. Even then, years ago, it was the only
animal in the world with two heads.

When the Famous Five go to stay on a lighthouse, they accidentally uncover hidden treasure. But unfortunately for them, someone out there thinks they know too much . . .

Timmy was standing with his nose towards the closed door of the room, his hackles rising up on his neck. He looked truly fierce!

'What on *earth* is the matter, Tim?' said Julian, going to the door. 'There can't be anyone on the stairway – the entrance door's jammed!'

Timmy raced out of the door as soon as Julian opened it and tore down the spiral stairway at such a speed that he fell, and rolled to the bottom. George gave a terrified scream. 'Timmy! Have you hurt yourself?'

But Timmy leapt to his feet at once, and ran to the entrance door, growling so ferociously that Anne felt really frightened. Julian ran down and went to the door. It was still well and truly jammed.

'Timmy! Maybe it's just the poor milkman, come with some milk again,' he said, and unjammed the door. He took hold of the handle to open it.

It wouldn't open! Julian pulled and tugged, but it was of no use. The door simply would NOT open!

By this time everyone was down beside him. 'Let *me* try,' said Dick. 'The door must just have stuck.'

No – he couldn't open it either! Julian looked gravely round at everyone. 'I'm afraid – very much afraid – that SOMEBODY has locked us in!' he said.

(Extract from *Five Go to Demon's Rocks* by Enid Blyton.)

Other favourite authors of 1970:
Charles Dickens, Agatha Christie,
Robert Louis Stevenson *(Treasure Island)*,
W. E. Johns *(Biggles* series).

Other favourite authors of 1995:
Roald Dahl, R. L. Stine, Judy Blume,
Stephen King.

Tanglewood Tales
by Nathaniel Hawthorne

These stories are based upon
Greek myth and legend.

from *The Minotaur*

*Since being defeated at war, the
people of Athens must send fourteen
young men and women to Crete
every year to be eaten by the
hideous Minotaur. But Prince
Theseus is determined to prevent
this and, with the help of Ariadne,
ventures into the winding labyrinth
to find the creature . . .*

He would have felt quite lost, and utterly hopeless of ever again walking in a straight path, if, every little while, he had not been conscious of a gentle twitch at the silken cord. Then he knew that the tender-hearted Ariadne was still holding the other end, and that she was fearing for him, and hoping for him, and giving him just as much of her sympathy as if she were close by his side. Oh, indeed, I can assure you, there was a vast deal of human sympathy running along that slender thread of silk. But still he followed the dreadful roar of the Minotaur, which now grew louder and louder, and finally so very loud that Theseus fully expected to come close upon him at every new zigzag and wriggle of the path. And at last, in an open space, at the very centre of the labyrinth, he did discern the hideous creature!

Sure enough, what an ugly monster it was! Only his horned head belonged to a bull; and yet, somehow or other, he looked like a bull all over, preposterously waddling on his hind legs; or, if you happened to view him in another way, he seemed wholly a man, and all the more monstrous for being so. And there he was, the wretched thing, with no society, no companion, no kind of a mate, living only to do mischief, and incapable of knowing what affection means. Theseus hated him, and shuddered at him, and yet could not but be sensible of some sort of pity; and all the more, the uglier and more detestable the creature was. For he kept striding to and fro in a solitary frenzy of rage, continually emitting a hoarse roar, which was oddly mixed up with half-shaped words; and, after listening a while, Theseus understood that the Minotaur was saying to himself how miserable he was, and how hungry, and how he hated everybody, and how he longed to eat up the human race alive.

> *Vividly written, telling stories which intrigued me; I could well picture the scenes and events which Hawthorne described. I still enjoy them!*
> **– Patrick Moore**

from Black Beauty
by Anna Sewell

I was quite happy in my new place, and if there was one thing that I missed, it must not be thought I was discontented; all who had to do with me were good, and I had a light airy stable and the best of food. What more could I want? Why, liberty! For three years and a half of my life I had had all the liberty I could wish for; but now, week after week, month after month, and no doubt year after year, I must stand up in a stable night and day except when I am wanted, and then I must be just as steady and quiet as any old horse who has worked twenty years. Straps here and straps there, a bit in my mouth, and blinkers over my eyes. Now, I am not complaining for I know it must be so. I only mean to say that for a young horse full of strength and spirit who has been used to some large field or plain, where he can fling up his head, and toss up his tail and gallop

away at full speed, then round and back again with a snort to his companions – I say it is hard never to have a bit more liberty to do as you like. Sometimes, when I have had less exercise than usual, I have felt so full of life and spring that vhen John has taken me out to exercise, I really could not keep quiet; do what I would, it seemed as if I must jump, or dance, or prance, and many a good shake I know I must have given him, specially at the first; but he was always good and patient.

'Steady, steady, my boy,' he would say; 'wait a bit and we'll have a good swing, and soon get the tickle out of your feet.' Then as soon as we were out of the village, he would give me a few miles at a spanking trot, and then bring me back as fresh as before, only clear of the fidgets, as he called them. Spirited horses, when not enough exercised, are often called skittish, when it is only play; and some grooms will punish them, but our John did not, he knew it was only high spirits.

It moved me deeply – the cruelty and the kindness. I read it again and again. I suppose it is a child-friendly book about the battle between good and evil – **Clare Short**

Life on the Scilly Isles in 1907 is bleak. Laura's brother has gone to sea, leaving the family to endure many hardships. Then one day Laura finds a washed-up turtle on the shore, and, in trying to save its life, finds some hope for her own.

I told him then all about Billy, about Joseph Hannibal and the *General Lee,* and about how I missed Billy so much, all about the cows dying and about how nothing had gone right since the day Billy left. When I looked across at him his eyes were closed. He seemed to be dozing in the sun. I'd been talking to myself.

The gulls never left us alone, not for a minute. They stood eyeing us from the rocks, from the shallows. When I threw stones at them now, they didn't fly off, they just hopped a little further away, and they always came back. I didn't go home for lunch – I just hoped Father wouldn't come looking for me. I couldn't leave my turtle, not with the gulls all around us just waiting their moment. Besides, the tide was coming in now, closer all the time. Then there was barely five yards of sand left between the sea and my turtle, and the water was washing up the channel just as I'd planned it. It was now or never.

I told him what he had to do.

'You've got to walk the rest,' I said. 'You want to get back in the sea, you've got to walk, you hear me?'

He tried. He honestly tried. Time and again he dug the edge of his flippers into the sand, but he just couldn't move himself.

The flippers dug in again, again, but he stayed where he was. I tried pushing him from behind. That didn't work. I tried moving his flippers for him one by one. That didn't work. I slapped his shell. I shouted at him. All he did was swallow once or twice and blink at me. In the end I tried threatening him. I crouched down in front of him.

'All right,' I said. 'All right. You stay here if you like. See if I care. You see those gulls? You know what they're waiting for? If they don't get you, then someone else'll find you and you'll be turtle stew.'

(Extract from *The Wreck of the Zanzibar* by Michael Morpurgo.)

from The Children of the New Forest
by Captain Marryat

*Their father having been killed fighting for
King Charles I, the four Beverley children find
refuge with old Jacob, deep in the New Forest.
But as the forester knows, there is much
to be learned . . .*

'I must bring them up to be useful – to depend on themselves; there is not a moment to be lost, and not a moment shall be lost; I will do my best, and trust to God. I ask but two or three years, and by that time I trust that they will be able to do without me. They must commence tomorrow the life of forester's children.'

Acting upon this resolution, Jacob, as soon as the children were dressed and in the sitting-room, opened his Bible, which he had put on the table, and said –

'My dear children, you know that you must remain in this cottage, that the wicked troopers may not find you out; they killed your father, and if I had not taken you away they would have burnt you in your beds. You must therefore live here as my children, and you must call yourselves by the name of Armitage, and not that of Beverley; and you must dress like children of the forest, as you do now, and you must do as children of the forest do – that is, you must do everything for yourselves, for you can have no servants to wait upon you. We must all work; but you will like to work if you all work together, for then the work will be nothing but play. Now, Edward is the oldest, and he must go out with me in the forest, and I must teach him to kill deer and other game for our support; and when he knows how, then Humphrey shall come out and learn how to shoot.'

'Yes,' said Humphrey, 'I'll soon learn.'

I admired the children's self-sufficiency and their ability to adapt to their forest life. The book has made a lasting impression on me in adult life
– Jon Snow

Top Books

Walk Two Moons by Sharon Creech won the W. H. Smith's Mind-Boggling Books Award in 1996, which is judged by children aged between 9 and 12. It also won the Children's Book Award (for a longer novel) and the Newbery Medal in 1995.

Sal is trying to make sense of a world from which her mother has suddenly, and without warning, disappeared. And when the mother of her best friend, Phoebe, decides to leave her family as well, it brings home Sal's own sense of loss.

'I have to go,' I said.

At the door, Phoebe said, 'My mother has disappeared. Sal, don't tell anyone. Don't tell a soul.'

At home, my father was slumped over the photo album. He used to close the album quickly when I came in the room, as if he were embarrassed to be caught with it. Lately, however, he didn't bother to close it. It was almost as if he didn't have the strength to do that.

On the opened page was a photo of my father

and mother sitting in the grass beneath the sugar maple. His arms were around her and she was sort of folded into him. His face was pressed up next to hers and their hair blended together. They looked like they were connected.

'Phoebe's mother went away,' I said.

He looked up at me.

'She left some notes She says she's coming back, but I don't believe it.'

I went upstairs and tried to work on my mythology report. My father came to the doorway and said, 'People usually come back.'

Now, I can see that he was just talking in general, just trying to be comforting, but then – that night – I heard in what he said the tiniest reassurance of something I had been thinking and hoping. I had been praying that a miracle would happen and my mother would come back and we would return to Bybanks and everything would be exactly as it used to be.

(Extract from *Walk Two Moons* by Sharon Creech.)

from Charlie and the Chocolate Factory
by Roald Dahl

*When Willy Wonka offers children
the chance to visit his wonderful chocolate
factory, everyone is desperate to find the
elusive Golden Ticket. But poor, starving
Charlie is simply desperate to eat some
of the chocolate that he can never
normally afford . . .*

Charlie went on wolfing the chocolate. He couldn't stop. And in less than half a minute, the whole thing had disappeared down his throat. He was quite out of breath, but he felt marvellously, extraordinarily happy. He reached out a hand to take the change. Then he paused. His eyes were just above the level of the counter. They were staring at the silver coins lying there. The coins were all five-penny pieces. There were nine of them altogether. Surely it wouldn't matter if he spent just one more . . .

'I think,' he said quietly, 'I think . . . I'll have

just one more of those chocolate bars. The same kind as before, please.'

'Why not?' the fat shopkeeper said, reaching behind him again and taking another Whipple-Scrumptious Fudgemallow Delight from the shelf. He laid it on the counter.

Charlie picked it up and tore off the wrapper . . . and *suddenly* . . . from underneath the wrapper . . . there came a brilliant flash of gold.

Charlie's heart stood still.

'It's a Golden Ticket!' screamed the shopkeeper, leaping about a foot in the air. 'You've got a Golden Ticket! You've found the last Golden Ticket! Hey, would you believe it!

Come and look at this, everybody! The kid's found Wonka's last Golden Ticket! There it is! It's right here in his hands!'

It seemed as though the shopkeeper might be going to have a fit. 'In my shop, too!' he yelled. 'He found it right here in my own little shop! Somebody call the newspapers quick and let them know! Watch out now, sonny! Don't tear it as you unwrap it! That thing's precious!'

> *This was the book I most enjoyed reading with my child. My daughter's name is Charlotte and I said to myself, if this doesn't help her to read nothing will. The book completely captivated us. Willy Wonka has to be one of the world's most fascinating characters –* ***Liccy Dahl***

Growing Up,
Breaking Out
Age 12 and over

from Tarka the Otter
by Henry Williamson

Tarka is a dog-cub and the eldest of the litter.
He and the other young otters have much to
learn about survival in the wild, including the
skills of swimming and catching fish . . .

The bitch took her cubs to a pool below the
bridge and walked with them across a
shallow tail of water. She stared at the stones,
brown and slippery with seaweed, and the cubs
stared also. They watched the glimmers in the
claws of water, sometimes trying to bite them.
While they were watching the mother ran along
the bank to the top of the pool and slid into the
water. More often than usual her head looked up
as she swam from bank to bank, for she was not
hunting, but driving the fish down to the cubs.
Tarka became excited and, seeing a fish, he swam
after it and went underwater to get it. In order to
travel faster, he struck out with all four webs
together, and lo! Tarka was swimming like an
otter near a fish. It was the biggest fish he had
seen, and although he kicked after it at the rate of

nearly two hundred kicks a minute, he lost it after a yard. He yikkered in his anger, and oh! Tarka was no longer swimming like an otter, but gasping and coughing on the surface, a poor little sick-feeling cub mewing for his mother.

He felt better when he had eaten a mullet caught by his mother. The fish had come up with the tide and remained in the still pool. Later in the night Tarka caught a pollywiggle, or tadpole, in a watery hoof-hole and thought himself a real hunter as he played with it, passing it from paw to paw and rolling on his back in the mud. He was quite selfish over his prey when his mother went to see what he was doing, and cried, *Iss-iss-ic-yang!* an old weasel threat, which being interpreted means, Go away, or I will drink your blood!

I loved, and still love, Tarka the Otter *for all sorts of reasons. For C. F. Tunnicliffe's wonderful woodcuts, for the setting of the book in a part of the West Country that I knew, for the otter lore that I learned from it, and, above all, for Williamson's beautiful evocation of a wonderful story –* **Dick King-Smith**

Top Books

Northern Lights by Philip Pullman won the Carnegie Medal in 1995 and was joint winner of the Guardian Children's Fiction Award in 1996.

When Lyra's friend, Roger, disappears she is determined to find him. The mysterious Mrs Coulter offers to take her to the frozen North, to where it is said all the missing children have been spirited away. But Lyra begins to wonder who she can really trust . . .

She remembered what she had to do and tapped on the glass door. It opened almost at once.

'Good girl. Come in quickly. We haven't got long,' said the Master, and drew the curtain back across the door as soon as she had entered. He was fully dressed in his usual black.

'Aren't I going after all?' Lyra asked.

'Yes; I can't prevent it,' said the Master, and Lyra didn't notice at the time what an odd thing that was to say. 'Lyra, I'm going to give you something, and you must promise to keep it private. Will you swear to that?'

'Yes,' Lyra said.

He crossed to the desk and took from a drawer a small package wrapped in black velvet. When he unfolded the cloth, Lyra saw something like a large watch or a small clock: a thick disc of brass and crystal. It might have been a compass or something of the sort.

'What is it?' she said.

'It's an alethiometer. It's one of only six that were ever made. Lyra, I urge you again: keep it private. It would be better if Mrs Coulter didn't know about it. Your uncle –'

'But what does it do?'

'It tells you the truth. As for how to read it, you'll have to learn by yourself. Now go – it's getting lighter – hurry back to your room before anyone sees you.'

He folded the velvet over the instrument and thrust it into her hands. It was surprisingly heavy. Then he put his own hands on either side of her head and held her gently for a moment.

She tried to look up at him, and said, 'What were you going to say about Uncle Asriel?'

'Your uncle presented it to Jordan College some years ago. He might –'

Before he could finish, there came a soft urgent knock on the door. She could feel his hands give an involuntary tremor.

'Quick now, child,' he said quietly. 'The powers of this world are very strong. Men and women are moved by tides much fiercer than you can imagine, and they sweep us all up into the current. Go well, Lyra; bless you, child; bless you. Keep your own counsel.'

(Extract from *Northern Lights* by Philip Pullman.)

from The Highwayman
by Alfred Noyes

The wind was a torrent of darkness among
the gusty trees;
The moon was a ghostly galleon tossed upon
cloudy seas,
The road was a ribbon of moonlight over the
purple moor,
And the highwayman came riding –
Riding – riding –
The highwayman came riding, up to the old
inn-door.

He'd a French cocked-hat on his forehead, a
bunch of lace at his chin,
A coat of the claret velvet, and breeches of
brown doeskin:
They fitted with never a wrinkle; his boots
were up to the thigh!
And he rode with a jewelled twinkle,
His pistol butts a-twinkle,
His rapier hilt a-twinkle, under the jewelled sky.

Over the cobbles he clattered and clashed in
  the dark inn-yard,
And he tapped with his whip on the shutters,
  but all was locked and barred:
He whistled a tune to the window; and who
  should be waiting there
But the landlord's black-eyed daughter,
  Bess, the landlord's daughter,
Plaiting a dark red love-knot into her long
  black hair.

---

*The poem combines a sense of romance and danger
that is heightened by its rhyming scheme and
rhythm – **Gareth Hale***

from Gormenghast
by Mervyn Peake

*The young Lord Titus lives with his family in
the cobwebbed kingdom of Gormenghast. But
within the dank castle walls arrives the presence
of something evil – and Titus gradually comes to
realize that dark forces are at work. On a walk
with his mother one day, he is confronted with
more evidence . . .*

She turned her head. She whistled again and
her whistle was answered, quick as an echo.
She gave the calls of a dozen birds and a dozen
voices echoed her with an insolent precision. The
birds about her feet and on her shoulders had
stiffened.

Her hand was gripping Titus' shoulder like an
iron clamp. It was all he could do not to cry out.
He turned his head with difficulty and saw his
mother's face – the face that had been so calm as
the snow itself. It had darkened.

It was no bird that was answering her; that
much she knew. Clever as it was, the mimicry
could not deceive her. Nor did it seem that

whatever gave vent to the varying calls was anxious to deceive. There had been something taunting about the rapidity with which each whistle of the Countess had been flung back from the wood.

What was it all about? Why was his arm being gripped? Titus, who had been fascinated by his mother's power over the birds, could not understand why the calls from the wood should have so angered her. For she trembled as she held him. It seemed as though she were holding him back from something, as though the wood was hiding something that might hurt him – or draw him away from her.

And then she lifted her face to the tree tops, her eyes blazing.

'Beware!' she cried and a strange voice answered her.

'*Beware!*' it called and the silence came down again.

> *This was my favourite book as a teenager – I just got sucked in by those strange, intense characters, all battling to be themselves. My favourite character was Steerpike – **Melvin Burgess***

Mid-Term Break

I sat all morning in the college sick bay
Counting bells knelling classes to a close.
At two o'clock our neighbours drove me home.

In the porch I met my father crying –
He had always taken funerals in his stride –
And Big Jim Evans saying it was a hard blow.

The baby cooed and laughed and rocked the
    pram
When I came in, and I was embarrassed
By old men standing up to shake my hand

And tell me they were 'sorry for my trouble'.
Whispers informed strangers I was the eldest,
Away at school, as my mother held my hand

In hers and coughed out angry tearless sighs.
At ten o'clock the ambulance arrived
With the corpse, stanched and bandaged by the
    nurses.

Next morning I went up into the room.
    Snowdrops
And candles soothed the bedside; I saw him
For the first time in six weeks. Paler now,

Wearing a poppy bruise on his left temple,
He lay in the four-foot box as in his cot.
No gaudy scars, the bumper knocked him clear.

A four-foot box, a foot for every year.

from The Lady of Shalott
by Alfred, Lord Tennyson

On either side the river lie
   Long fields of barley and of rye,
That clothe the wold and meet the sky;
And through the field the road runs by
     To many-tower'd Camelot;
And up and down the people go,
Gazing where the lilies blow
Round an island there below,
     The island of Shalott.

Willows whiten, aspens quiver,
Little breezes dusk and shiver
Through the wave that runs for ever
By the island in the river
     Flowing down to Camelot.
Four gray walls, and four gray towers
Overlook a space of flowers,
And the silent isle embowers
     The Lady of Shalott.

By the margin, willow-veil'd,
Slide the heavy barges trail'd
By slow horses; and unhail'd
The shallop flitteth silken-sail'd
     Skimming down to Camelot:
But who hath seen her wave her hand?
Or at the casement seen her stand?
Or is she known in all the land,
     The Lady of Shalott?

Only reapers, reaping early
In among the bearded barley,
Hear a song that echoes cheerly
From the river winding clearly,
     Down to tower'd Camelot:
And by the moon the reaper weary,
Piling sheaves in uplands airy,
Listening, whispers ''Tis the fairy
     Lady of Shalott.'

---

*Having the irresistible rhythms and the stunning
Pre-Raphaelite imagery they conjure put into
my head when young has been a lasting
pleasure, something I would want for any child*
– Shirley Hughes

from White Fang
by Jack London

*In the frozen wilds of north-west Canada, a
wolf-cub finds himself the only survivor of a
litter. He is thrust into a savage world where
each day becomes a fight to stay alive.*

He sat up and gazed about him, as might the
first man of the earth who landed upon
Mars. The cub had broken through the wall of the
world, the unknown had let go its hold of him,
and here he was without hurt. But the first man
on Mars would have experienced less
unfamiliarity than did he. Without any
antecedent knowledge, without any warning
whatever that such existed, he found himself an
explorer in a totally new world.

Now that the terrible unknown had let go of
him, he forgot that the unknown had any
terrors. He was aware only of curiosity in all the
things about him. He inspected the grass
beneath him, the moss-berry plant just beyond,

and the dead trunk of the blasted pine that stood
on the edge of an open space among the trees. A
squirrel, running around the base of the trunk,
came full upon him, and gave him a great fright.
He cowered down and snarled. But the squirrel
was as badly scared. It ran up the tree, and from
a point of safety chattered back savagely.

This helped the cub's courage, and though the
woodpecker he next encountered gave him a

start, he proceeded confidently on his way. Such was his confidence, that when a moose-bird impudently hopped up to him, he reached out at it with a playful paw. The result was a sharp peck on the end of his nose that made him cower down and ki-yi. The noise he made was too much for the moose-bird, who sought safety in flight.

But the cub was learning. His misty little mind had already made an unconscious classification. There were live things and things not alive. Also, he must watch out for the live things. The things not alive remained always in one place; but the live things moved about, and there was no telling what they might do. The thing to expect of them was the unexpected, and for this he must be prepared.

I think this brings alive both the glory and the cruelty of nature. It also illustrates the cruelty of man and the majesty of animal life around us. It has both emotion and stimulation and I think offers an excellent read. Jack London is a superb author
– David Blunkett

from The Lord of the Rings
by J. R. R. Tolkien

Middle Earth is under threat from the forces of Darkness. Little does Frodo realize that he holds in his hands the key to the future of the land he loves. But the young hobbit comes closer to understanding when the wizard, Gandalf, reveals the secrets of the ring . . .

To Frodo's astonishment and distress the wizard threw it suddenly into the middle of a glowing corner of the fire. Frodo gave a cry and groped for the tongs; but Gandalf held him back.

'Wait!' he said in a commanding voice, giving Frodo a quick look from under his bristling brows.

No apparent change came over the ring. After a while Gandalf got up, closed the shutters outside the window, and drew the curtains. The room became dark and silent, though the clack of Sam's shears, now nearer to the windows, could still be heard faintly from the garden. For a moment the wizard stood looking at the fire; then he stooped and removed the ring to the hearth with the tongs, and at once picked it up. Frodo gasped.

'It is quite cool,' said Gandalf. 'Take it!' Frodo received it on his shrinking palm: it seemed to have become thicker and heavier than ever.

'Hold it up!' said Gandalf. 'And look closely!'

As Frodo did so, he now saw fine lines, finer than the finest penstrokes, running along the ring, outside and inside: lines of fire that seemed to form the letters of a flowing script. They shone piercingly bright, and yet remote, as if out of a great depth.

'I cannot read the fiery letters,' said Frodo in a quavering voice.

'No,' said Gandalf, 'but I can. The letters are Elvish, of an ancient mode, but the language is that of Mordor, which I will not utter here. But this in the Common Tongue is what is said, close enough:

One Ring to rule them all, One Ring to find them,
One Ring to bring them all and in the darkness bind them.

It is only two lines of a verse long known in Elven-lore:

Three Rings for the Elven-kings under the sky,
   Seven for the Dwarf-lords in their halls of stone,
Nine for Mortal Men doomed to die,
   One for the Dark Lord on his dark throne
In the Land of Mordor where the Shadows lie.
   One Ring to rule them all, One Ring to find them,
   One Ring to bring them all and in the darkness
      bind them
In the Land of Mordor where the Shadows lie.'

He paused, and then said slowly in a deep voice: 'This is the Master-ring, the One Ring to rule them all. This is the One Ring that he lost many ages ago, to the great weakening of his power. He greatly desires it – but he must *not* get it.'

Frodo sat silent and motionless. Fear seemed to stretch out a vast hand, like a dark cloud rising in the East and looming up to engulf him. 'This ring!' he stammered. 'How, how on earth did it come to me?'

Acknowledgements

The editor and publishers gratefully acknowledge the following for permission to reproduce copyright extracts and illustrations in this book:

Five Minutes' Peace by Jill Murphy, published by Walker Books, copyright © Jill Murphy, 1986, reprinted by permission of Walker Books Ltd, London; *Owl at Home* by Arnold Lobel, published by World's Work Ltd 1976, copyright © Arnold Lobel, 1975, reprinted by permission of World's Work (a division of Reed Int. Books Ltd); *Dogger* by Shirley Hughes, published by The Bodley Head, Random House UK Ltd 1977, copyright © Shirley Hughes, 1977, reprinted by permission of the publisher; *Green Eggs and Ham*™ by Dr Seuss, published in the UK by HarperCollins by arrangement with Random House, Inc., New York, USA, copyright © Dr Seuss Enterprises, L.P. 1960 and 1998. All rights reserved, reprinted by permission of the publishers; *Schnitzel von Krumm's Basketwork* by Lynley Dodd, published by Mallinson Rendel Publishers Ltd 1994, copyright © Lynley Dodd, 1994, reprinted by permission of Mallinson Rendel Publishers Ltd, Wellington, N.Z. and Lynley Dodd; *Rupert the Bear Annual 1945* by Alfred Bestall, published by Express Newspapers 1945, Rupert™ copyright © Express Newspapers Plc, 1998; *Lottie's Letter* by Gordon Snell, published by Orion Children's Books 1996, copyright © Gordon Snell, 1996, reprinted by permission of the publisher; *Peter Pan and Wendy* by J.M. Barrie, published by Hodder & Stoughton 1911, copyright © Great Ormond Street Children's Hospital, 1929, reprinted by permission of Great Ormond Street Children's Hospital, illustration copyright © Elsa Trimby, 1986, reprinted by kind permission of Elsa Trimby; 'The Little Mermaid' by Hans Christian Andersen from *Hans Andersen's Fairy Tales* retold by Jean Robertson, published by Blackie & Son Limited 1961, copyright © Blackie & Son Limited, 1961, reprinted by permission of the publisher, illustrations copyright © Shirley Hughes, 1961, reprinted by kind permission of Shirley Hughes; *It Was a Dark and Stormy Night* by Janet and Allan Ahlberg, published by Viking 1993, copyright © Janet and Allan Ahlberg, 1993, reprinted by kind permission of Allan Ahlberg; 'Waiting at the Window' from *Now We Are Six* by A.A. Milne, published by Methuen & Co. Ltd 1927, copyright © A.A. Milne,1927, reprinted by permission of Reed Consumer Books; line illustration by E.H. Shepard from *Now We Are Six*, copyright under the Berne Convention, reprinted by permission of Curtis Brown, Ltd; 'The Ugly Duckling' by Hans Christian Andersen from *Hans Andersen's Fairy Tales* retold by Jean Robertson, published by Blackie & Son Limited 1961, copyright © Blackie & Son Limited, 1961, reprinted by permission of the publisher, illustrations copyright © Shirley Hughes, 1961, reprinted by kind permission of Shirley Hughes; *The Wind in the Willows* by Kenneth Grahame, published by Methuen 1931, copyright © The University Chest, Oxford, reprinted by permission of Curtis Brown Ltd, line illustration by E.H. Shepard from *The Wind in the Willows*, copyright under the Berne Convention, reprinted by permission of Curtis Brown Ltd; *The Hundred-Mile-an-Hour Dog* by Jeremy Strong, published by Viking 1996, text copyright © Jeremy Strong, 1996, reprinted by kind permission of Jeremy Strong;

Index of Celebrities